FIVE THINGS TO FIND

Retold by Verna Wilkins and Gill McLean

Acknowledgements

David Scott Cowan
BBC Producer, Science Challenge

Frank Flynn
BBC Education Officer

Sita Ramamurthy
Story Researcher

Barry Wilkinson
Illustrator

Piloting
Davies School, Leytonstone
Camberley First School

and finally
Paul, Rhys, Huw, Nicki, Heidi, John and Penny
Thanks for your co-operation and support

Tamarind Books

© Tamarind 1991   ISBN 1-870516-07-9   Printed in Singapore
This impression 1999

Once upon a time in Tunisia, there lived a wise man.
He had three children.

The first was called Hassan. He was enormously tall and strong.
He was the strongest boy that anyone had ever seen.
He could pull a plough or a heavy cart all by himself.
He could pick up a massive family tent,
hoist it onto his head and walk for miles.
He could make a path through the forest
by knocking down trees with his bare hands.

Everyone was amazed by him.

The second child was called Yasmin. She was incredibly fast.
She was the fastest girl that anyone had ever seen.
She was always busy, running here and there,
carrying messages and bringing news.
She could run so fast that she could race a deer
or a cheetah, and win.
She could even race the wind.

Everyone was astounded by her.

The third child was called Fatima. She wasn't tall,
she wasn't strong, and she wasn't fast. She was clever.
She liked reading, counting and measuring things.
She spent a lot of time by herself, solving problems and
working out sums.

Everyone felt sorry for her, because she was little and shy.

One day their father called them all together and said,
'There is something I would like you to do for me.'

'Is it a heavy task?' asked Hassan,
bending and stretching and
flexing his muscles.
He was ready to take on the toughest job
his father could give him,
and he couldn't wait to begin.

'Can we start now?' asked Yasmin,
getting ready to run.
She couldn't wait to show her father
how quickly she could work.

'Oh,' said Fatima, 'Tell us what it is!'

'Not so fast' said their father. 'Stop and listen carefully.
It is a difficult task and you should work together.
If you do, you will all succeed.'

'I want you to bring me five things.
First, a roof for my house.
Second, some rope to tie the roof on.
Third, some food to celebrate with.
Fourth, some bowls to eat out of.
And last, but not least, some water. It must be so pure
that it has never seen the light of day, or
been touched by human hands.'

Hassan, Yasmin and Fatima looked at each other in surprise,
but their father hadn't finished yet.
'You have just three days to find all these things,'
he continued. 'You can start whenever you like,
but you must be back here by the end of the third day.'

'I see,' said Hassan. 'I can find them all myself.
First, a roof ...
Hm! With my strength, I can manage that easily.
Don't worry girls. You stay here. I don't need you.
I won't be long.'
He rushed out of the house into the hot sun.

In the forest he found some tall, straight trees.
He knocked them down with his bare hands
and broke off the branches.
By the end of the first day, he had stacked them all
in a neat pile in the clearing he had made.
He stood looking at the trees
and felt very pleased with himself.

He was just imagining his father telling him what a good job he'd done,
when he remembered that there were some other things to collect as well.
He tried to think what else his father had said.
At last he remembered.

Some rope to tie the roof on.
Some food to celebrate with.
Some bowls to eat out of.
And some water. It must be so pure that it has never seen
the light of day, nor been touched by human hands.

Hassan didn't have a clue where to find any of those things,
but he didn't stop to think.
He spent the next two days pacing about in the forest,
looking up and down, behind rocks and under bushes and getting nowhere.
He wished he hadn't boasted about how quickly he could finish the task.
He wished they had all worked together.

Soon after Hassan had dashed off into the forest, Yasmin jumped up.
'Don't worry Fatima,' she said, 'I can run really quickly.
I'm so fast that I can race the wind. I don't need you.
You just sit there and wait. I can do this on my own.'

She ran out into the hot sun without glancing back.
She ran north for miles and miles, until she found some metal
that would make a good roof. She picked it up and turned round.
Then she ran south for miles and miles until she found some wire
to hold the roof together.
By that time it was evening, and she was exhausted.
She was sorry she'd boasted about how fast she was.
She put down the metal roof and the wire and went to sleep.

The next morning she woke up, ready to go again.
Only three more things to find, she thought.
She picked up the metal roof and the wire, and turned to the east.
She ran for miles and miles, until she came to a river,
and there she stopped.

She made pots with clay from the river bank.
She found a bush bearing beautiful berries and gathered some of them.
Yasmin was feeling very pleased with herself.

She started counting the things she had found.
A roof for the house.
Some wire to tie the roof on.
Some food to celebrate with.
Some bowls to eat out of.

What had she forgotten?
She hadn't found the pure water!
She had no idea where to find water that had never seen the light of day
nor been touched by human hands.
She spent all that day and the next running about
looking in ponds and puddles. She couldn't find pure water anywhere.

At last she decided to return home, as it was getting late.
She picked up the metal and the wire, the bowls and the berries
and raced for home.
She ran so fast that the bowls broke and all the berries fell out,
leaving a trail behind her.

Fatima was still at home. She had stayed in the cool of the garden,
while the others were rushing about in the sun.
'It's the last day. Aren't you going too?'
asked her father gently.
'I'm thinking,' said Fatima.

She stood in the garden, leaned against one of the coconut trees
and looked up at the sky. It was cool under the tree.
The sun was shining through the leaves,
making dappled patterns on the sand.
Right above her was a big bunch of coconuts.
She thought about the tree, the coconuts
and the enormous green leaves. She looked up at them again and again.
She suddenly realized that she knew exactly what to do.

What do you think Fatima's plan was?

She worked in the shade under the tree, all day long.
In the evening, she went back to the house.

Hassan was there,
looking hot, weary and dirty.
He had branches to make the roof,
but that was all.

Yasmin was there.
She too was very tired
and was resting her sore feet
on the cool tiles.
She had the roof and the rope.
The pots were broken, the berries had all been lost,
and she hadn't found the water.

18

However, Fatima had everything her father wanted.

First, a roof for the house.
Coconut leaves woven together make a good roof.

Second, some rope to tie the roof on.
Coconut fibre, twisted or woven, makes strong rope.

Third, some food to celebrate with.
Coconut is very tasty to eat.

Fourth, some bowls to eat out of.
Coconuts, split in half, make fine bowls.

And last, but not least, some water.
Inside a coconut is pure, clean water that is protected by
the fibrous skin and the hard shell of the nut.
It can never see the light of day, nor be touched by human hand,
until the nut is cracked open.

Hassan looked at Fatima.
How had she found all the things, even though she wasn't big and strong?
Hassan was amazed.

Yasmin, too, looked at Fatima.
How had she managed it all, even though she wasn't fast?
Yasmin was astounded.

Their father smiled and said, 'Fatima isn't tall,
she isn't strong, and she can't run fast. However, she knows how to think.'
He put his arms around them and said, 'This task was difficult,
but it could have been done more easily.
You are all very special but in different ways,
and you need to work together.
You need Hassan's strength, Yasmin's swiftness and
Fatima's careful thought. Then you will be a wonderful team.'

After that Hassan, Yasmin and Fatima did everything together
and nothing was too difficult for them.

How did Fatima know what to do?

Hassan and Yasmin rushed off straight away but Fatima didn't. She sat quietly in the garden.

She spent time thinking about the job. She planned what she was going to do. She saw that she could use the tree to make everything she needed.

She worked all day collecting, cutting, plaiting, twisting. By the evening everything was ready.

Now you can try the same problem.
Imagine that you are lost in the mountains. You have to find:-
      a shelter
      some food
      some bowls to eat out of
      some pure clean water.
What would you do?

Look at some fruits and vegetables. What are they like outside?
Carefully cut them open (across or down).
Can you draw them? Try printing with them.

Look at a corner of your park or playground. Are they any
plants or animals living there? Are there any differences
between wet and dry places? Are there any differences between
sunny places and shady places?
Draw a plan of where everything is.

Grow some seeds: cress, broad beans or mung beans.
Put some in a dark place and some in a bright place.
Keep some damp and some dry. Do they all grow?

Hassan, Yasmin and Fatima live in Tunisia. Where is it?
What is the weather like there? What do people wear?
What do they eat?